A Book of
Christmas
Carols

Illustrated by Gill Guile

Brimax Books · Newmarket · England

Jingle Bells

Dashing through the snow
In a one-horse open sleigh,
O'er the fields we go,
Laughing all the way,
Bells on bob-tail ring,
Making spirits bright,
What fun it is to ride and sing
A sleighing song tonight.

Jingle bells! Jingle bells!
Jingle all the way,
Oh, what fun it is to ride
In a one-horse open sleigh,
Jingle bells! Jingle bells!
Jingle all the way,
Oh, what fun it is to ride
In a one-horse open sleigh.

Now the ground is white
Go it while you're young.
Take the girls tonight,
Sing this sleighing song.
Get a bob-tailed bay,
Two-forty for his speed.
Then hitch him to an open sleigh,
And you will take the lead.

Good King Wenceslas

Good King Wenceslas looked out
On the Feast of Stephen,
When the snow lay round about,
Deep and crisp and even;
Brightly shone the moon that night,
Though the frost was cruel,
When a poor man came in sight,
Gathering winter fuel.

"Hither, page, and stand by me,
If thou know'st it, telling,
Yonder peasant, who is he?
Where and what his dwelling?"
"Sire, he lives a good league hence,
Underneath the mountain,
Right against the forest fence,
By Saint Agnes' fountain."

"Bring me flesh and bring me wine,
Bring me pine logs hither;
Thou and I will see him dine,
When we bear them thither."
Page and monarch forth they went,
Forth they went together,
Through the rude wind's wild lament
And the bitter weather.

"Sire, the night is darker now,
And the wind blows stronger;
Fails my heart, I know not how,
I can go no longer."
"Mark my footsteps, good my page!
Tread thou in them boldly:
Thou shalt find the winter's rage
Freeze thy blood less coldly."

In his master's steps he trod,
Where the snow lay dinted;
Heat was in the very sod
Which the saint had printed.
Therefore, christian men be sure,
Wealth or rank possessing,
Ye who now will bless the poor,
Shall yourselves find blessing.

The First Noel

The first Noel the angels did say
Was to certain poor shepherds in fields as they lay;
In fields where they lay, keeping their sheep,
In a cold winter's night that was so deep.
Noel, Noel, Noel, Noel,
Born is the King of Israel!

They looked up and saw a star,
Shining in the east, beyond them far;
And to the earth it gave great light,
And so it continued both day and night.
Noel, Noel, Noel, Noel,
Born is the King of Israel!

And by the light of that same star,
Three wise men came from country far;
To seek for a king was their intent,
And to follow the star wherever it went.
Noel, Noel, Noel, Noel,
Born is the King of Israel!

This star drew nigh to the north-west;
O'er Bethlehem it took its rest,
And there it did stop and stay
Right over the place where Jesus lay.
Noel, Noel, Noel, Noel,
Born is the King of Israel!

O Christmas Tree

O Christmas Tree, O Christmas Tree,
With lush green boughs unchanging –
Green when the summer sun is bright,
And when the forest's cold and white.
O Christmas Tree, O Christmas Tree,
With lush green boughs unchanging.

O Christmas Tree, O Christmas Tree,
Here once again to awe us,
You bear round fruits of Christmas past,
Spun out of silver, gold and glass.
O Christmas Tree, O Christmas Tree,
Here once again to awe us.

O Christmas Tree, O Christmas Tree,
You fill the air with fragrance,
You shrink to very tiny size,
Reflected in the children's eyes.
O Christmas Tree, O Christmas Tree,
You fill the air with fragrance.

O Christmas Tree, O Christmas Tree,
We gladly bid you welcome.
A pyramid of light you seem,
A galaxy of stars that gleam.
O Christmas Tree, O Christmas Tree,
We gladly bid you welcome.

O Christmas Tree, O Christmas Tree,
What presents do you shelter?
Rich wrappings hide the gifts from sight,
Done up in bows and ribbons tight.
O Christmas Tree, O Christmas Tree,
What presents do you shelter?

O Christmas Tree, O Christmas Tree,
Your green limbs teach a lesson:
That constancy and faithful cheer
Are gifts to cherish all the year.
O Christmas Tree, O Christmas Tree,
Your green limbs teach a lesson.

I Saw Three Ships

I saw three ships come sailing by,
Come sailing by, come sailing by,
I saw three ships come sailing by,
On Christmas Day in the morning.

And what do you think was in them then,
Was in them then, was in them then?
And what do you think was in them then,
On Christmas Day in the morning?

Three pretty girls were in them then,
Were in them then, were in them then,
Three pretty girls were in them then,
On Christmas Day in the morning.

One could whistle, and one could sing,
And one could play on the violin;
Such joy there was at my wedding,
On Christmas Day in the morning.

O Little Town of Bethlehem

O little town of Bethlehem,
How still we see thee lie!
Above thy deep and dreamless sleep
The silent stars go by:
Yet in the dark streets shineth
The everlasting Light;
The hopes and fears of all the years
Are met in thee to-night.

For Christ is born of Mary;
And, gathered all above,
While mortals sleep, the angels keep –
Their watch of wondering love.
O morning stars, together
Proclaim the holy birth,
And praises sing to God the King,
And peace to men on earth.

How silently, how silently,
The wondrous gift is given!
So God imparts to human hearts
The blessings of the heaven.
No ear may hear his coming;
But in this world of sin,
Where meek souls will receive him still —
The dear Christ enters in.

O holy Child of Bethlehem,
Descend to us, we pray;
Cast out our sin, and enter in:
Be born in us today,
We hear the Christmas angels —
The great glad tidings tell:
O come to us, abide with us,
Our Lord Emmanuel.

We Three Kings

We three Kings of Orient are,
Bearing gifts we traverse afar,
Field and fountain, moor and mountain,
Following yonder star.

O, star of wonder,
Star of night,
Star with royal beauty bright,
Westward leading, still proceeding,
Guide us to Thy perfect light.

Melchior:
Born a King on Bethlehem plain,
Gold I bring, to crown Him again,
King forever, ceasing never,
Over us all to reign.

Caspar:
Frankincense to offer have I;
Incense owns a deity nigh:
Prayer and praising, all men raising,
Worship Him, God most high.

Balthazar:
Myrrh is mine, its bitter perfume
Breathes a life of gathering gloom;
Sorrowing, sighing, bleeding, dying,
Sealed in a stone-cold tomb.

Glorious now behold Him arise,
King, and God, and sacrifice!
Heaven sings alleluia,
Alleluia the earth replies.

God Rest Ye Merry, Gentlemen

God rest ye merry, gentlemen,
Let nothing you dismay,
For Jesus Christ our Saviour
Was born on Christmas Day,
To save us all from Satan's power
When we were gone astray.
O tidings of comfort and joy,
Comfort and joy,
O tidings of comfort and joy!

In Bethlehem in Jewry
This blessed babe was born,
And laid within a manger
Where oxen feed on corn,
And Mary knelt and prayed to God
Upon that blessed morn.
O tidings of comfort and joy,
Comfort and joy,
O tidings of comfort and joy!

From God our Heavenly Father
A host of angels came
Unto some certain shepherds
With tidings of the same,
That there was born in Bethlehem
The Son of God by name.
O tidings of comfort and joy,
Comfort and joy,
O tidings of comfort and joy!

Silent Night

Silent night, holy night,
All is calm, all is bright
Round yon virgin Mother and Child,
Holy infant, so tender and mild.
Sleep in heavenly peace,
Sleep in heavenly peace.

Silent night, holy night,
Darkness flies, all is light.
Shepherds hear the angels sing,
"Alleluia, hail the King!
Jesus the Saviour is born,
Jesus the Saviour is born."

Silent night, holy night,
Wondrous star, lend thy light;
With the angels let us sing
Alleluia to our king.
Christ the Saviour is born,
Christ the Saviour is born.

Joy to the World

Joy to the world! The Lord is come;
Let earth receive her King;
Let ev'ry heart prepare Him room,
And heav'n and nature sing,
And heav'n and nature sing,
And heav'n, and heav'n and nature sing.

Joy to the earth! The Saviour reigns;
Let men their songs employ;
While fields and floods, rocks, hills and plains
Repeat the sounding joy,
Repeat the sounding joy,
Repeat, repeat the sounding joy.

No more let sins and sorrows grow,
Nor thorns infest the ground;
He comes to make His blessings flow
Far as the curse is found,
Far as the curse is found,
Far as, far as the curse is found.

He rules the world with truth and grace,
And makes the nations prove
The glories of His righteousness,
And wonders of His love.
And wonders of His love,
And wonders, and wonders of His love.

Hark! The Herald Angels Sing

Hark! The herald angels sing,
Glory to the newborn King;
Peace on earth and mercy mild,
God and sinners reconciled;
Joyful all ye nations rise,
Join the triumph of the skies,
With th'angelic host proclaim,
Christ is born in Bethlehem.
Hark! the herald angels sing,
Glory to the new-born King!

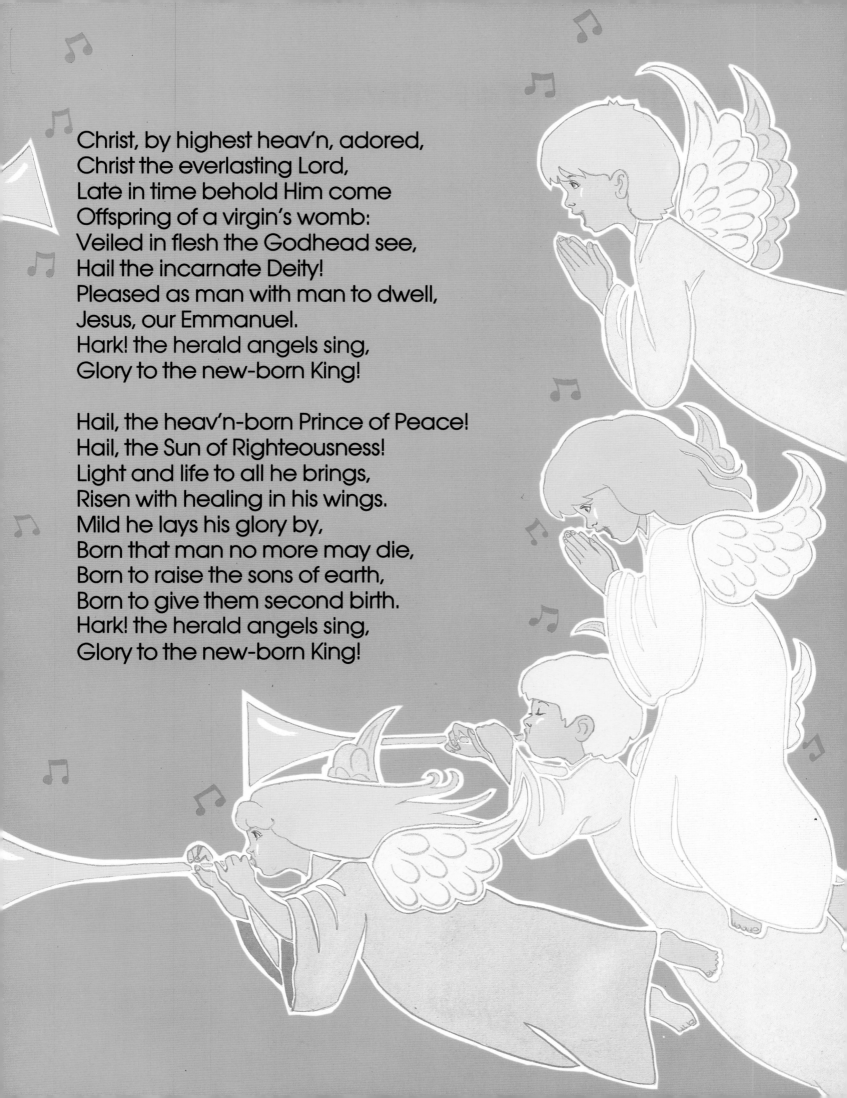

Christ, by highest heav'n, adored,
Christ the everlasting Lord,
Late in time behold Him come
Offspring of a virgin's womb:
Veiled in flesh the Godhead see,
Hail the incarnate Deity!
Pleased as man with man to dwell,
Jesus, our Emmanuel.
Hark! the herald angels sing,
Glory to the new-born King!

Hail, the heav'n-born Prince of Peace!
Hail, the Sun of Righteousness!
Light and life to all he brings,
Risen with healing in his wings.
Mild he lays his glory by,
Born that man no more may die,
Born to raise the sons of earth,
Born to give them second birth.
Hark! the herald angels sing,
Glory to the new-born King!

O Come, All Ye Faithful

O come, all ye faithful,
Joyful and triumphant,
O come ye, o come ye to Bethlehem;
Come and behold Him;
Born the King of angels;

O come, let us adore Him,
O come, let us adore Him,
O come, let us adore Him,
Christ the Lord!

Sing, choirs of angels,
Sing in exultation;
O sing, all ye citizens of heav'n above;
'Glory to God
In the highest.'

O come, let us adore Him,
O come, let us adore Him,
O come, let us adore Him,
Christ the Lord!

Christmas is Coming

Christmas is coming,
The geese are getting fat,
Please put a penny
In the old man's hat.
If you haven't got a penny,
A ha'penny will do;
If you haven't got a ha'penny,
Then God bless you!

We Wish You a Merry Christmas

We wish you a Merry Christmas,
We wish you a Merry Christmas,
We wish you a Merry Christmas,
And a Happy New Year!

Glad tidings we bring
To you and your kin.
We wish you a Merry Christmas,
And a Happy New Year.

Away in a Manger

Away in a Manger, no crib for a bed,
The little Lord Jesus laid down His sweet head.
The stars in the bright sky looked down where He lay:
The little Lord Jesus asleep on the hay.

The cattle are lowing, the baby awakes,
But little Lord Jesus, no crying He makes.
I love Thee, Lord Jesus! Look down from the sky,
And stay by my bedside till morning is nigh.

Be near me Lord Jesus; I ask Thee to stay
Close by me forever and love me, I pray.
Bless all the dear children in Thy tender care,
And fit us for heaven, to live with Thee there.